The bear wants to go for a ride.
He sits in the wagon.

The boy pulls.
The bug pushes.

The wagon does not move.
The bear is too big.

This time, the bug pulls
and the boy pushes.

The wagon still does not move.
The bear has an idea.

He gets out of the wagon.
He pulls it to the top
of a hill.

They all go for a ride.

Then he gets back in.
The bug and the boy get in, too.